Human Sexuality
A Responsible Approach

Author
Linda A. Berne, Ed.D., CHES
Department of Health Promotion and Kinesiology
The University of North Carolina at Charlotte

Dr. Berne is a professor of health education at the University of North
Carolina at Charlotte. A former middle school health and science teacher,
Dr. Berne serves as a consultant and speaker on teen sexuality issues.

Content Consultants
Allison L. Greenspan, M.P.H.
Health and Medical Communications
  Consultant
Former Senior Writer-Editor for the
  Centers for Disease Control and
  Prevention (CDC)
Atlanta, Georgia

Julius B. Richmond, M.D.
John D. MacArthur Professor of Health
  Policy
Director, Division of Health Policy
  Research and Education
Harvard University
Advisor on Child Health Policy
Children's Hospital of Boston
Boston, Massachusetts

ScottForesman

A Division of HarperCollinsPublishers

Editorial Office: Glenview, Illinois
Regional Offices: Sunnyvale, California • Tucker, Georgia
Glenview, Illinois • Oakland, New Jersey • Dallas, Texas

Reviewers

Picture Credits

Page 6: James Ewing. Page 9 (l): W. S. Nawrocki/Nawrocki Stock Photo. Page 11: Joseph A. DiChello, Jr. Page 16: John Walsh, Science Photo Library/Photo Researchers. Page 25: Joseph A. DiChello, Jr. Page 27: SIU/Photo Researchers. Page 31 (l): Yoav/Phototake. Page 33: Prof. Luc Montagnier, Institut Pasteur/CNRI/Science Photo Library/Photo Researchers. Page 36: Courtesy Centers for Disease Control. Page 38: Dept. of Medical Photography, St. Stephen's Hospital, London/Science Photo Library/Photo Researchers. Page 39: Dennis Zucharzak. Page 41: Will/Deni McIntyre/Phototake. Page 42 (t): CNRI/Science Photo Library/Photo Researchers. Page 42 (b): CDC/Science Source/Photo Researchers. Page 43 (t): CNRI/Science Photo Library/Photo Researchers. Page 43 (b): Biophoto Associates/Science Source/Photo Researchers. Pages 47, 48: Don and Pat Valenti.

All photographs not credited are the property of Scott, Foresman and Company.

Illustrations: © Teri J. McDermott, Clinical Assistant Professor, University of Illinois Medical Center.

Contents

To the Student:

As you grow and develop during adolescence, you will experience many changes and new situations. This booklet will help you understand those changes and become prepared for many of the new situations you will encounter.

ACCURATE INFORMATION To make wise decisions, you need sound, accurate information. In this booklet you will learn the facts about how you develop physically and become a sexually mature person. You will also learn how you mature mentally, emotionally, and socially. Since not all of these changes occur at the same time, you will probably experience many uncertainties as you go through your teen years. You may experience pressures from others to become sexually active. In order to make healthy decisions, you need to learn about the problems that can develop from becoming sexually active at a young age. You need accurate information about the consequences of teenage pregnancy and the health effects of AIDS and other sexually transmitted diseases. You will learn why the surest way to avoid these problems is abstinence—saying no to intimate sexual activities.

LIFE SKILLS In order to deal with the changes and pressures of adolescence, you need to develop life management skills. In this booklet you will learn ways to cope with pressure from peers to do things you do not want to do. You will learn refusal skills—ways to say no. You will learn communication skills, which will help you express yourself clearly and give the right messages. You will also learn about goal setting and decision making. You will learn how to make decisions using a five-step model. You will see how decision-making skills can help you solve problems as you go through adolescence and prepare for adulthood.

When you were a young child, you depended on others to provide for your needs. As you went through childhood, you gradually took on more responsibility for meeting your needs. Now you need to prepare for adulthood when you will take full responsibility for your life. This booklet provides you with both the accurate information and the skills you will need to make the best decisions for a healthy life.

Adolescence: A Time of Change

These teenagers are launching hundreds of balloons. Each balloon carries a postcard with a message and the sender's address. They hope the wind currents will carry their balloons far away. Perhaps the person who finds their balloon will write them a postcard in return. Like these teenagers, you will have many new experiences as you go through adolescence. Adolescence is a time of growing and developing, changing, learning, choosing, and having fun.

Changes During Adolescence

adolescence (ad'l es'ns), the period of life between childhood and adulthood.

During your teenage years, you go through the period of life between childhood and adulthood known as **adolescence**. Young people experience adolescence between the ages of 11 and 21. It is a time of many changes in your life, especially physical changes. As your body grows and develops, your feelings also grow and change or develop. Like the people studying together in this picture, you may form different relationships with those around you.

Adolescence is also a time of learning. You will have many questions about the changes in your body. You may hear many explanations, but some of these are only rumors, and you may not know what to believe. As you read this booklet, you will find reliable answers to many of your questions, and you will be able to sort out any misinformation you get from other sources.

In this chapter, you will learn about changes that teenagers experience as they go through adolescence. You will learn how these changes and the development of life management skills lead to more independence and responsibility.

As you become an adult, you will take on more responsibility for your own health, education, and financial well-being. Your physical, mental, emotional, and social growth during adolescence will prepare you for these responsibilities of adulthood. The adult who emerges from adolescence is very different from the child who entered it some years earlier.

Physical Growth

The beginning of adolescence is marked by a **growth spurt**. Most girls begin their growth spurt between the ages of 9 and 13, and for most boys it starts between the ages of 11 and 15. The time of this growth spurt varies for each person because it is determined largely by heredity. No matter when it starts, everyone will reach his or her adult size by the end of adolescence.

The time during adolescence when a boy or girl becomes sexually mature is called **puberty**. The reproductive organs of sexually mature people have grown and begun to function as organs of adults. Sexually mature people are capable of having children.

At a time that is right for you, your body releases chemicals called **hormones** into your bloodstream. These hormones start the growth and development that takes place during puberty. Other hormones cause the sex glands—**ovaries** in girls and **testes** in boys—to mature. When the testes and ovaries mature, they also make and release hormones. These hormones cause the body changes that make girls and boys develop into women and men.

Look at the changes that occur in a girl's body in the picture below. During puberty, most girls' hips widen and breasts grow larger. One breast may grow to be slightly larger than the other, even after maturity. Hair grows in the pubic area and under the arms. Girls' voices may become a little deeper.

growth spurt, a time of rapid growth that begins adolescence.

puberty (pyü′bər tē), the time during adolescence when a boy or a girl becomes sexually mature.

hormones (hôr′mōnz), chemicals produced by the body that affect or control the activity of some body organs.

ovaries (ō′vər ēz), sex glands in the female that produce eggs.

testes (tes′tēz), sex glands in the male that produce sperm.

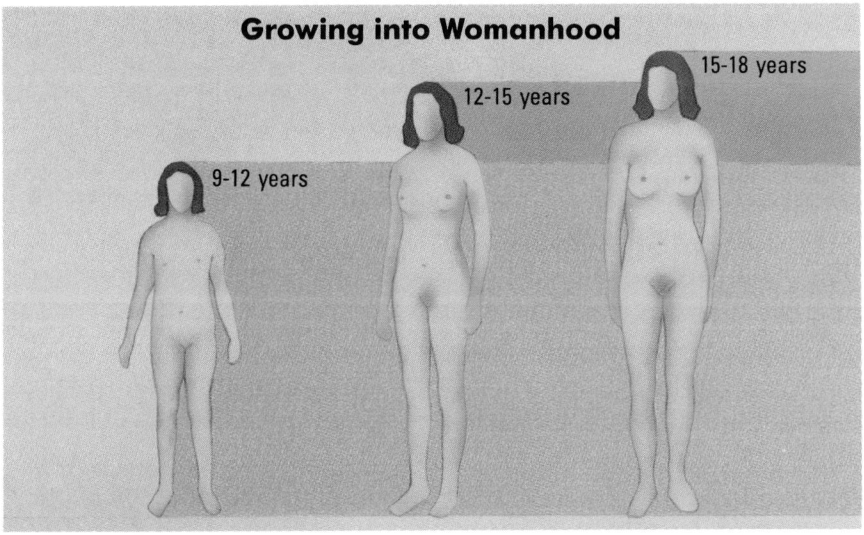

Growing into Womanhood

9-12 years
12-15 years
15-18 years

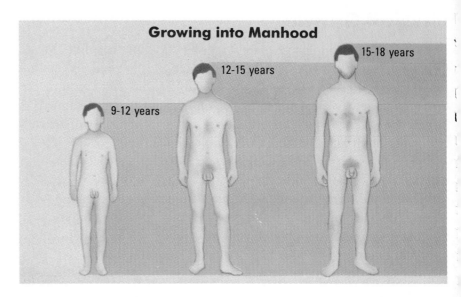

Growing into Manhood

9-12 years

12-15 years

15-18 years

Look at the picture of the changes in a boy's body as he grows to manhood. During puberty, boys' shoulders become broader. Hair grows on the face and chest, under the arms, and in the pubic region. Most boys also experience sudden voice changes as their vocal cords grow and their voices become deeper.

During puberty, the reproductive organs mature and produce sex cells—eggs in females and sperm in males. You will learn more about the reproductive organs and sex cells in Chapter 2.

Mental and Emotional Growth

The physical growth that you experience during adolescence is accompanied by mental and emotional growth. As you grow mentally, you begin to understand abstract ideas that were too difficult when you were younger. You begin trying many new things to learn about your talents and interests. As you discover what you like to do, you will learn how these talents and interests may lead to hobbies or careers. You begin to understand more about yourself and how you are unique.

You can learn many skills during your teenage years. As you learn these skills, you gain self-confidence. Whether you choose to repair a motor or learn to play a musical instrument, like the teenagers in the photographs, you are developing skills and talents that you will use throughout your life.

Emotional growth also occurs during adolescence. Some emotional changes are related to levels of hormones in the body. Sudden shifts in certain hormones can trigger feelings of anxiety, irritability, restlessness, or lack of motivation. At times you might feel very happy or sad and not know why. You might have outbursts of anger that surprise you. These are normal adolescent feelings, and learning to manage them is part of growing up.

Because their bodies are changing so fast, many teenagers have new feelings about the way they look. Teenagers sometimes feel self-conscious about new body features or their physical maturity compared to others. Often teenagers develop acne or need to wear braces. Learning to accept changes in yourself and to deal with problems is a big part of growing up. Mature people are able to feel anger, disappointment, or frustration without shouting, hitting, or throwing things.

Social Growth

As you grow physically, mentally, and emotionally during your teenage years, you will also develop more social skills. Many boys and girls become interested in members of the opposite sex during their teen years. Sometimes a boy and a girl form a close relationship. They enjoy spending a lot of time together.

Teens might go to group activities together such as dances and ball games. As they grow older, they might also go to the movies or a dance just as a couple. Teens might date and feel strong affection for more than one person over four or five years. Dating different people during adolescence helps teens learn which qualities they like and helps them develop social skills. Teens can enjoy dating without getting involved in sexual activity. Saying no to sexual intercourse and other intimate sexual activities is called **abstinence**.

abstinence (ab′stə nəns), saying no to sexual intercourse and other intimate sexual activity.

Developing Responsibility

As you develop more independence during the teen years, you will also develop more responsibility. Practicing abstinence, treating all people with respect, and considering other people's needs and wishes are all an important part of social responsibility. Developing life management skills and your own set of values will help you become an independent, responsible adult.

During adolescence, you begin to think more about what is important to you and what is not important. For example, education may be very important to someone who wants to become a teacher. Ideas about what is important to you are your **values**.

values, ideas about what is important or not important in life.

Values, such as a sense of right and wrong, are usually learned from families. As you go through adolescence, you will also learn about the major values of society and how society sets guidelines for standards of behavior. Values that are expected of everyone are called universal values. Some universal values include honesty, loyalty to family and country, the search for truth, and treating others as you want to be treated. These values, combined with your own set of values, will guide your behavior throughout your life.

As you become more independent during adolescence, you will develop a set of values that will guide your behavior. You will also learn about the values of your friends and peers—people your age. Learning to accept and respect the values of other people while upholding your own is an important part of social maturity. Mature people recognize that others have feelings, rights, opinions, and property that should be respected. People who are not socially mature think only of their own rights and needs.

As teenagers learn about their own values, they also find that their relationships with friends often change. They begin to look for friends who can provide help when needed and who approve of their own values. Therefore, their friends might change. They learn that true friends will accept you even if you do not always do or say what they want. Learning to do what you think is right, and resisting pressure from friends and peers to behave in ways that are not true to your values, are important life management skills.

Besides the change in relationships with their friends, teenagers find that their relationships with their parents change during adolescence. When you were younger, most decisions about your life were probably made for you. You depended heavily on your family, and you were given few responsibilities. As you grew older, you became a bit more independent. As you move through adolescence and show a more mature attitude, you will be allowed to make more of your own decisions. The life skills you learn during adolescence will help you develop more responsibility for your life.

As adolescents become adults, they need more than physical, emotional, and social maturity. They need to be able to take on adult responsibilities. Adults need an education to be able to take care of themselves financially. Getting a high school diploma is necessary for most full-time jobs. Many students, like the graduates pictured below, choose to get more training through vocational schools, technical schools, colleges, or universities. A person with a good education and a variety of skills will have more opportunity for job success. Then he or she is more likely to become a fully independent, responsible adult.

Chapter 1 Review

Part I. Write the numbers 1–8 on your paper. Match each definition in Column A with a term from Column B.

Column A

1. sex glands in the female
2. the part of adolescence when a boy or girl matures sexually
3. the period of life between childhood and adulthood
4. chemicals that affect or control the activity of some organs
5. saying no to sexual intercourse and intimate sexual activity
6. sex glands in the male
7. time of rapid growth
8. ideas about what is important in life

Column B

a. abstinence
b. adolescence
c. growth spurt
d. hormones
e. ovaries
f. puberty
g. testes
h. values

Part II. Write the numbers 9–20 on your paper. Answer the following in complete sentences.

9. What chemicals cause the growth spurt to occur?
10. What are four physical changes girls experience in puberty?
11. What are four physical changes boys experience in puberty?
12. What are four types of growth that adolescents experience?
13. How do the mental abilities of adolescents differ from those of younger children?
14. Explain what sometimes triggers sudden shifts in feelings in teenagers.
15. How do mature people handle anger, disappointment, or frustration?
16. How do sexually mature people behave towards others?
17. Name two benefits of dating different people.
18. Give an example of a value.
19. Give two signs of social responsibility.
20. How do relationships with parents often change during adolescence?

Chapter

2

Human Reproduction

This father enjoys watching his daughter learn and grow. She has many features like his, and some features like her mother. The child has traits of both parents because her development began with the joining of two sex cells, one from each parent. The mature reproductive systems of a father and mother are needed to produce offspring. In this chapter, you will read about the male and female reproductive systems and how they function to produce a new human being.

Male Reproductive Organs

genitals (jen′ə təlz), sex organs located outside the body.

penis (pē′nis), male reproductive organ located outside the body.

scrotum (skrō′təm), pouch that contains the testes.

foreskin (fôr′skin′), fold of skin that covers the glans.

glans (glanz), tip of the penis.

circumcision (ser′kəm sizh′ən), surgical operation to remove the foreskin from the penis.

Some of the male reproductive organs are located outside the body. Sex organs located outside the body are called **genitals**. The male's genitals, shown below, are the **penis** and the **scrotum**. The scrotum is a pouch behind the penis and contains the testes. The penis, like other organs, grows during puberty. The size of the penis varies from person to person, but size is not important to its function.

The head of the penis is called the **glans**. At birth, a male has a cover of thin, loose skin over the glans. This fold of skin is called the **foreskin**. Shortly after birth, some parents ask their doctor to surgically remove the boy's foreskin in an operation called **circumcision**. Males who are not circumcised should be careful to pull back the foreskin when they bathe. Cleaning the area under the foreskin will help keep bacteria from growing there and causing an infection.

Sperm, the male sex cells, are made inside the testicles, also called testes. One testicle might be larger and hang lower than the other. Uneven growth is not a cause for concern. Testicles sometimes appear to change size because of the movement of a layer of muscles below the skin in the scrotum. When the scrotum is exposed to cold air or cold water, the muscles draw the testicles close to the body. In warm environments, the scrotum hangs loosely because warmth relaxes the muscles in the scrotum. This keeps the temperature at a level needed for sperm development.

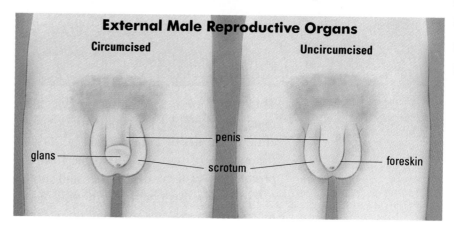

External Male Reproductive Organs

Circumcised

Uncircumcised

glans — penis — foreskin

scrotum

Functions of the Male Reproductive Organs

The inside of the penis is made of spongy tissue with many blood vessels. The tip of the penis, the glans, has many nerve endings and is very sensitive. Most of the time, a male's penis is soft and limp. When a penis is stimulated, blood fills the spongy tissues. The penis then stiffens and extends away from the body. This normal bodily function is called an **erection**.

Another normal bodily function in males is a **nocturnal ejaculation**, or wet dream. An ejaculation occurs when the semen is released during an erection. A wet dream happens while a man is asleep. Only about a teaspoon of sticky, milk-colored fluid passes onto bedclothes or sheets. There is no reason to feel upset or worried when this happens. Wet dreams are not controllable. A man might experience wet dreams many times during his life, once in a while, or not at all. All of these experiences are normal.

Men need to be careful to protect their reproductive organs from injury. They can wear protective cups or straps, such as an athletic supporter, during vigorous activity. Men should wear this protective equipment when they play such contact sports as football, baseball, basketball, hockey, or soccer. Such precautions will help protect the testes and penis from injury.

erection (i rek′shən), stiffening of the penis when the spongy tissue fills with blood.

nocturnal ejaculation (nok tėr′nl i jak′yə lā′shən), release of semen from the penis during sleep.

Male Sex Cells

During puberty, the testicles begin to make sperm. Testicles contain a great number of coiled tubes. These tubes are where the sex cells, or the sperm, are made. Each coiled tube is from one to three feet long. It takes about 60 days for a sperm to form in a testicle. The average male produces about 300 million sperm each day. Sperm continue to mature as they travel through the male reproductive system. Sperm production begins at puberty and goes on throughout a male's lifetime.

epididymis (ep'i did'ə mis), organ above each testicle where sperm become mature enough to fertilize an egg.

vas deferens (vas def'ər enz), either of two long tubes between the epididymis and the prostate gland.

seminal vesicles (sem'ə nəl ves'ə kəl), two glands that give off a fluid that mixes with sperm and contains nutrients.

prostate (pros'tāt) **gland,** large gland surrounding the male urethra in front of the bladder.

semen (sē'mən), fluid made in male reproductive organs that contains sperm.

urethra (yü rē'thrə), tube through which both semen and urine leave the male body.

Use the diagram on page 17 to follow the path sperm take through the male reproductive system. Sperm are carried from the testicles through small tubes to the **epididymis** above and behind each testicle. After sperm have been in the epididymis for 18 hours to 10 days, they become mature enough to fertilize an egg.

From each epididymis, the sperm enter a long tube called a **vas deferens**. Each of these tubes leads up into the body and over the bladder. Notice the wide part of the vas deferens in the small diagram. This is where most sperm are stored for as little as a few hours to as long as several months. Under each widened section of the vas deferens is a tiny gland. These glands are the **seminal vesicles**. Sperm move from the vas deferens into a single tube that runs through the **prostate gland**. The seminal vesicles give off a fluid into this tube. The fluid contains nutrients and offers protection for the sperm.

As the sperm, now mixed with fluid from the seminal vesicles, move into the tube that runs through the prostate gland, the prostate also gives off a fluid. The mixture of fluids and sperm in the tube is called the **semen**.

Semen moves through the prostate gland into a tube called the **urethra**. The urethra runs through the penis. Both urine and semen leave the body through the urethra, but not at the same time. Urine is stored in the bladder. A muscle closes the connection between the urethra and bladder when semen enters the urethra.

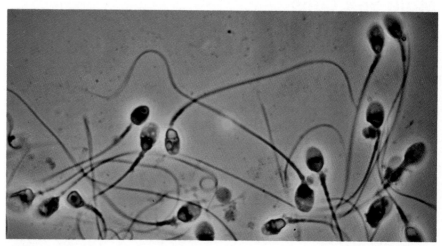

Sperm can only be seen through a microscope. These sperm are magnified 400 times.

Sperm are some of nature's smallest living cells. Look at the sperm in the photo to the left. Notice how each sperm has a round-like head, a thick middle part, and a long tail. Once released inside the female reproductive system, a sperm is able to move its tail. The motion of the tail allows sperm to swim toward a ripened egg.

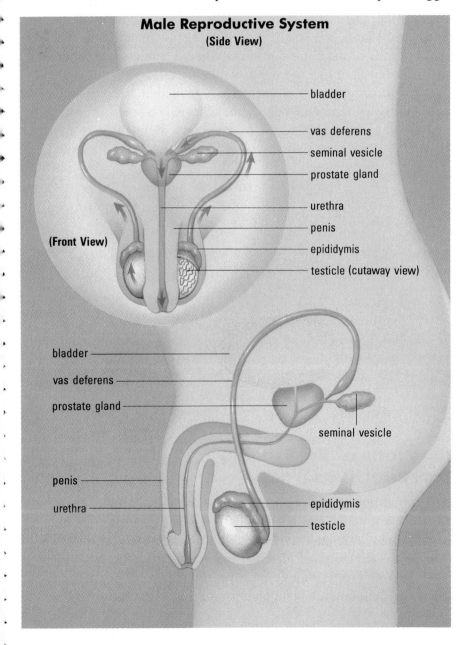

Male Reproductive System
(Side View)

- bladder
- vas deferens
- seminal vesicle
- prostate gland
- urethra
- penis
- epididymis
- testicle (cutaway view)

(Front View)

- bladder
- vas deferens
- prostate gland
- seminal vesicle
- penis
- urethra
- epididymis
- testicle

Female Reproductive Organs

The pictures show the female reproductive organs. The organs located inside the body are protected by a ring of bone called the **pelvic girdle**. The sex organs outside the body are called genitals.

The female genitals are protected by two narrow folds of skin called **labia**. The inside surfaces of the labia are moist with mucus. Between the labia is a small, bulb-like organ—the **clitoris**. The head or glans of the clitoris has many nerve endings and blood vessels. It is sensitive like the penis of the male.

Two body openings are near the genitals but not part of the reproductive system. Just behind the clitoris is a small opening, the urethra, where urine leaves the female body. Behind the opening of the vagina is the anus, where bowel movements leave the body.

pelvic (pel′vik) **girdle,** a ring of bone that protects the female reproductive organs located inside the body.

labia (lā′bē ə), folds of skin covering the outer opening of the vagina.

clitoris (klit′ər is), female genital organ at the top of the vulva with many nerve endings and blood vessels.

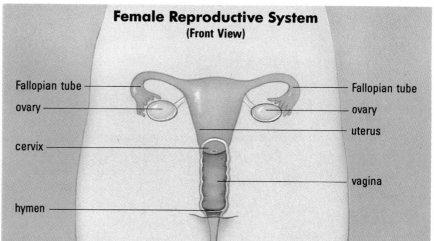

Female Reproductive System
(Front View)

Fallopian tube

ovary

cervix

hymen

Fallopian tube

ovary

uterus

vagina

Functions of the Female Reproductive Organs

Each of the female sex organs has a special function. Beginning at puberty, the ovaries produce female hormones and eggs. One of the hormones, **estrogen**, is responsible for the development of female traits such as broad hips and mature breasts. The other hormone, **progesterone**, mainly prepares the uterus for possible pregnancy and the breasts for supplying milk for a newborn baby.

estrogen (es′trə jən), a hormone responsible for the development of female traits.

progesterone (prō jes′tə rōn), a hormone responsible for preparing the uterus for possible pregnancy.

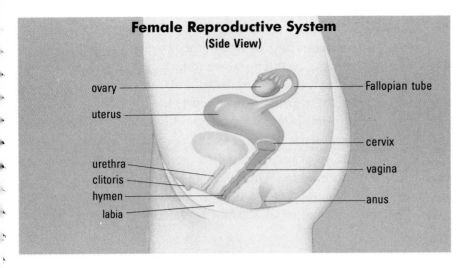

Female Reproductive System
(Side View)

ovary — — Fallopian tube

uterus —

— cervix

urethra —
clitoris —
hymen — — vagina
labia — — anus

Look at the diagrams of the female reproductive system. The two **Fallopian tubes** extend from the top of the uterus toward the ovaries. Eggs released from the ovaries travel through the Fallopian tubes to the uterus. The **uterus**, or womb, is a hollow, pear-shaped organ that lies between the two ovaries. The uterus holds the developing baby before birth. The uterus is a muscular organ that usually is about three inches long, about the size of a girl's fist, but it stretches when the baby grows and develops inside.

At the end of pregnancy, the uterus will have stretched enough to hold a fully developed baby. A baby ready to be born usually is about 15 to 20 inches long and weighs about 6 to 10 pounds. Soon after the baby is born, the uterus returns to its original size.

The lower end of the uterus is called the **cervix**. The cervix, sometimes called the neck of the uterus, is connected to the end of a passage called the **vagina**. The vagina leads to the outside of the body. During birth, a baby is pushed from the uterus through the cervix and passes out of the mother's body through the vagina. Find the cervix and vagina in the illustration on this page.

At the opening of the vagina is a thin ring of tissue called the **hymen**. The hymen partially covers the vagina passageway. It is very common for a girl to stretch or break her hymen during vigorous activities such as exercise. This is normal. A broken hymen does not harm the function of the reproductive system.

Fallopian (fə lō′pē ən) **tubes,** the female sex organs through which eggs pass to reach the uterus.

uterus (yü′tər əs), the female sex organ in which a baby develops.

cervix (sėr′viks), the lower end of the uterus that opens to the vagina.

vagina (və jī′nə), the female sex organ through which a baby passes during birth.

hymen (hī′mən), a ring of tissue inside the opening of the vagina.

Female Sex Cells

follicle (fol′ə kəl), a case of tissue enclosing an egg.

At birth, a girl has thousands of immature sex cells, called eggs, inside her two ovaries. Each egg lies within a case called a **follicle**. Throughout childhood, the eggs remain immature. About a year after the beginning of a girl's growth spurt, her pituitary gland, located at the base of the brain, starts sending hormones to her ovaries. The hormones signal the eggs in the ovaries to begin to mature. Every month, in either the right or the left ovary, an egg and its follicle begin to mature. When the egg is mature, the follicle breaks open. The egg leaves the follicle and moves away from the ovary. This process, called **ovulation**, is shown below.

ovulation (ō′vyə lā′shən), the egg's leaving of the ovary.

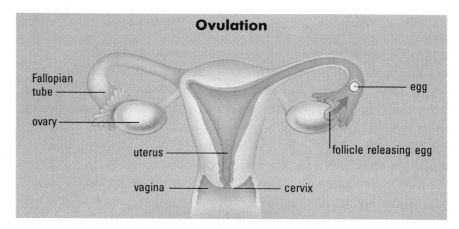

Ovulation

Fallopian tube

ovary

uterus

vagina

cervix

egg

follicle releasing egg

cilia (sil′ē ə), tiny hairlike structures that move in a beating motion.

After the egg moves away from the ovary, it enters the nearby Fallopian tube. The inside surfaces of the Fallopian tubes are covered with **cilia**. These tiny hairlike structures move in a beating motion. The motion of the cilia draws the released egg into the Fallopian tube and keeps it moving toward the uterus.

fertilization (fėr′tl ə zā′shən), the joining of a sperm with an egg.

As the egg moves through a Fallopian tube toward the uterus, **fertilization** can take place. Fertilization is the joining of a male sex cell—the sperm—with an egg. After fertilization takes place, the fertilized egg grows and develops into a baby. All the eggs that enter the Fallopian tube are not fertilized. If no sperm are present in the Fallopian tube, fertilization cannot take place.

Ovulation—Menstruation Cycle Each month, before an egg leaves the ovary, a hormone is sent to the uterus. This hormone signals for certain changes to take place in the lining of the uterus. Glands and blood vessels in the lining grow in preparation for a fertilized egg. If fertilized, the egg will attach itself to the thickened, blood-rich lining and begin to develop into a baby. The lining of the uterus helps to nourish the developing baby.

If the egg is not fertilized during the previous month, the special lining is not needed. Some of the blood and tissue of the lining pass out of the body through the vagina. The flow of these materials from the body is called menstruation. The time when menstruation is taking place is called the **menstrual period**. The length of the menstrual period varies from person to person, and from month to month. The average menstrual period is about five days. However, it can range from two to eight days.

During the days of menstruation, about two ounces of tissue and blood are lost. Usually, a loss of blood is a sign of injury. Menstruation, however, is a sign of health. Menstruation is a normal process that occurs when there is no fertilized egg to grow in the lining of the uterus. The body has no use for the blood and tissue that are lost through menstruation.

Two types of products are available to absorb the menstrual flow. Sanitary pads, or sanitary napkins, are worn outside of the body in underwear. The pad soaks up the flow and protects clothing. Tampons are tight rolls of fiber. A tampon is inserted into the vagina to absorb the menstrual flow before the flow leaves the body. A string on the end of the tampon is left hanging for easy removal of the tampon. Sanitary pads and tampons should be changed several times a day. A tampon should never be left in place for more than a few hours. Bathing frequently will help reduce body odors during the menstrual period.

The time span between the first day of one menstrual period and the first day of the next is called the **ovulation-menstruation cycle**, or O-M cycle. When a girl first starts to ovulate and menstruate, her cycle may be irregular. Many females eventually develop a regular cycle, which ranges from about 26 to 32 days. Ovulation usually occurs around the midpoint of the cycle, but ovulation can vary from person to person, and from period to period. No one can know exactly when ovulation is taking place.

menstrual period
(men′strü əl pir′ē əd), the time during which a female releases unneeded blood and tissue from the uterus.

ovulation-menstruation cycle, or O-M cycle, the time span between the beginning of one menstrual period and the beginning of the next.

Fertilization

When you are physically, emotionally, and socially mature, you might decide to marry. A husband and wife share deep feelings for each other. These feelings cause them to have a strong desire to show affection by hugging, kissing, and touching each other. These acts can cause the husband and wife to become sexually excited.

When the husband is sexually excited, he has an erection. When the wife is sexually excited, the muscles of her vagina relax. Her vagina and labia become moist with a clear fluid. When both partners are ready, **sexual intercourse** might take place. To have sexual intercourse, the husband inserts his erect penis into the wife's vagina. The liquid of the vagina makes it easy for the penis to enter. During intercourse ejaculation usually occurs.

Millions of sperm pass into the vagina during ejaculation. Look at the diagram to find out how fertilization takes place. When an egg is fertilized, pregnancy begins for the woman.

Fertilization does not happen every time a husband and wife have intercourse. An egg is released from an ovary only about once a month. The egg moves into a Fallopian tube where it stays for about a day. If live sperm are not present, the egg will begin to break down. Menstruation follows in about 14 days, and the unfertilized egg leaves the body along with unneeded blood and tissue.

sexual intercourse (sek′shü əl in′tər kôrs), the inserting of the erect penis into the vagina.

Signs of Pregnancy

First Month
- unprotected intercourse one or more times during last menstrual cycle
- missed menstrual period or slight spotty period
- tingling or pain in breasts
- dark area around nipple gets darker or changes color
- morning sickness or nausea
- fatigue

Second Month
- second missed menstrual period
- frequent urination
- retention of fluid and swelling
- weight gain

Third Month
- third missed menstrual period
- enlargement of abdomen
- abdominal stretch marks

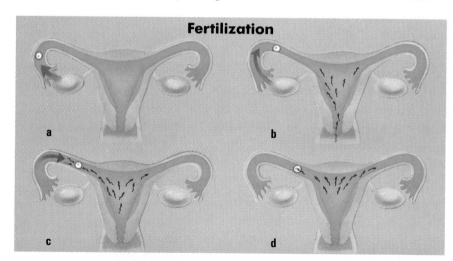

Fertilization

a: Egg is released from follicle and swept into Fallopian tubes. b: Ejaculated sperm move up from vagina through uterus into Fallopian tube. c: Sperm can live for about 3 days. They move toward egg. d: One sperm joins with the egg.

2 weeks

1 month

2 months

3 months

The Developing Baby

As soon as an egg is fertilized, it begins to change and grow. The egg divides and forms new cells until it becomes a small clump of cells. The cluster of dividing cells reaches the uterus in about three days. There the cluster of cells attaches itself to the lining of the uterus. At the place of attachment, the **placenta** begins to form. The placenta is a blood-rich organ made from tissues lining the uterus. It is the organ through which materials are exchanged between the mother and baby. Inside the placenta a sac filled with a water-like fluid cushions and protects the developing baby.

The baby is connected to the placenta by the umbilical cord. The cord contains blood vessels and goes into the baby's abdomen. Nutrients pass from the mother's blood to the placenta. They then move through the umbilical cord and enter into the baby's blood. Wastes from the baby's blood travel through the cord to the mother. The blood of the mother and the blood of the baby do not mix. But the blood vessels of each are so close together that many substances—including nutrients, oxygen, drugs, and pathogens—can cross over from the mother's blood into the baby's blood.

It usually takes nine months for the baby to develop. During that time, both baby and mother experience many changes. Having a doctor's care during pregnancy is very important. The doctor will explain ways to help the woman and her developing baby stay healthy. This type of care is called **prenatal**—''before birth''—**care**. Look at the drawings to see how a baby develops.

placenta (plə sen′tə), a blood-rich organ through which materials are exchanged between the mother and developing baby.

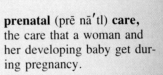

4 months

prenatal (prē nā′tl) **care,** the care that a woman and her developing baby get during pregnancy.

5-6 months

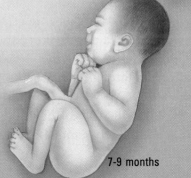

7-9 months

23

Chapter 2 Review

Part I. Write the numbers 1–10 on your paper. Match each definition in Column A with a term from Column B.

Column A

1. the joining of sperm with an egg
2. medical care a woman receives during pregnancy
3. organ made from tissues of the uterus
4. the egg's leaving of the ovary
5. fluid made in male reproductive organs that contains male sex cells
6. the period when a baby develops in a mother's uterus
7. pouch that contains the testes
8. case of tissue enclosing an egg
9. tube through which both semen and urine leave the male body
10. female sex organ in which a baby develops

Column B

a. fertilization
b. follicle
c. ovulation
d. placenta
e. pregnancy
f. prenatal
g. scrotum
h. semen
i. urethra
j. uterus

Part II. Write the numbers 11–20 on your paper. Answer the following in complete sentences.

11. When do males produce sperm?
12. How does the role of estrogen differ from that of progesterone?
13. What two things must be present in the Fallopian tubes for fertilization to take place?
14. Explain how fertilization of an egg affects the process of the menstruation.
15. How do muscles in the scrotum affect the appearance of the testes?
16. About how long is a menstrual cycle?
17. How does a developing baby receive food and oxygen?
18. Put these terms in the order in which an unfertilized egg travels through them: cervix, uterus, follicle, Fallopian tube, vagina.
19. Explain the role of blood in an erection.
20. What role do seminal vesicles play in reproduction?

3

Preventing Teenage Pregnancy

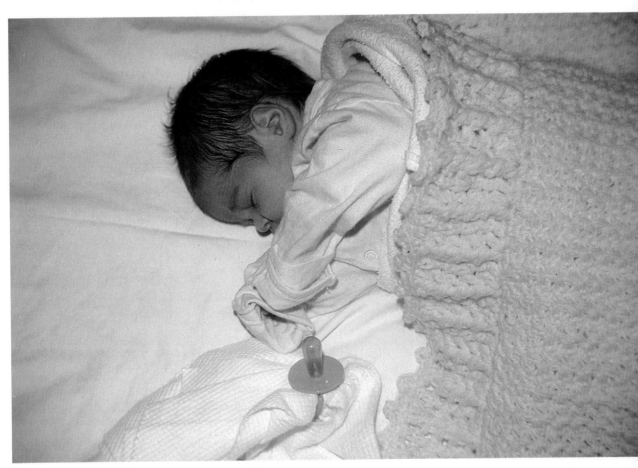

Although this newborn baby is healthy, it was born with a serious handicap. Both of its parents are teenagers not much older than you. The teenagers were physically mature enough to become parents, but they still lack other types of maturity to provide for their baby's needs. As a result, life will probably be more difficult for this baby and its parents.

Consequences of Teenage Pregnancy

Experts believe that one in ten teenage girls become pregnant each year. Four girls out of ten will become pregnant before they finish high school. The number of pregnant teenagers in the United States is about twice as high as in Canada, England, France, Sweden, and other developed countries. For many reasons, teenage **pregnancy** is a serious problem.

pregnancy (preg′nən sē), the period of time when a baby develops in a woman's uterus.

Social Problems For most teenagers, pregnancy is not a planned event. Because it happens before teenagers are ready for a family, many unexpected changes occur in their lives. Studies show that teenage mothers and fathers often drop out of school. The demands of being a parent and the need for money make it difficult for them to continue their education.

Because teenage parents have less schooling and often are single parents, many young fathers or mothers and their children live in poverty. They often have little money for good housing or health care. Teenage families might have to rely on government assistance to live. Studies show that teenage parents are more likely to abuse their children than parents who are older. Abused children often grow up to be abusive parents. Teenage pregnancy can be a costly problem to the community in many ways.

Sometimes the father and mother marry because of the baby. Studies show, however, that such marriages usually end in divorce. Most of the time, the father and mother do not marry. The teen mother and baby then usually live with the teen's family. In these cases, the teenage mother and her parents often disagree over who serves as the parent of the baby. Since the teen mother is still living in her parents' home, she does not have final say when it comes to herself or her baby. She also may be torn between meeting her own needs, such as doing things with her friends, and meeting the baby's needs.

The teen father experiences difficulties also. As an absent father, his role is uncertain. More and more, family courts are deciding that unmarried teenage fathers have a place in a child's life. The court expects a father to support the child in both nurturing and financial ways.

Health Problems Based on physical maturity, most doctors think the healthiest time to have a baby is between the ages of 20 and 30. Women under the age of 20 are still growing and have not yet reached physical maturity. Because of this, pregnancy during teenage years can cause physical problems for both mothers and babies.

Some of the problems with teenage pregnancies start with poor nutrition. Since both the mother and the baby are growing and developing, both need plenty of nutritious food. Getting enough of the right foods can be difficult.

Another problem for teenage mothers involves early deliveries. Teenage mothers have more **miscarriages** and premature babies than older mothers. Premature babies have a lower birth weight and are more likely to have health problems than babies born after the full nine months. Teenage mothers also spend more time in labor and often experience difficulties in delivery.

miscarriage, (mis kar′ij), the involuntary ending of a pregnancy before the developing baby can live outside of the mother's body.

Many other health concerns face a teenage mother and her developing baby. By seeking early prenatal care, some of these problems can be solved. The teenage mother in the picture has been seeing her doctor since the second month of her pregnancy.

Regular visits to a doctor throughout pregnancy can help solve and prevent problems for the mother and baby.

Pregnancy forces teenagers into adult roles before they are ready, which is unhealthy for them and for the child they create. Teenagers lack the physical, emotional, and social maturity to take on the responsibilities of parenthood. If you were a baby and could choose your own parents, how old would you want your parents to be? What other features would you choose in a parent? These are some of the questions you might think about as you become an adult.

Avoiding Teenage Pregnancy

Anyone who has sexual intercourse risks becoming pregnant, even with the best types of contraception—prevention of pregnancy. The surest way to avoid a pregnancy and other problems, such as sexually transmitted diseases, is abstinence.

Abstinence means saying no to sexual intercourse and other intimate sexual behavior. Sometimes teenagers are afraid to say no to their boyfriends or girlfriends out of fear of rejection. Young people depend on their friendships for security and a sense of belonging. However, true friends respect each other's feelings and limits of behavior and will not force their friends to go against their values. You will learn more about how to stay abstinent later in this chapter and how to cope with peer pressure in Chapter 6.

Being pregnant should be a happy occasion for a husband and wife. For a teenage boy and girl, pregnancy can be a crisis. You can plan ahead and avoid this crisis by becoming aware of how to prevent pregnancy. Talk to your parents, school counselor, nurse, or clergy about pressures or questions concerning pregnancy. Find out what resources are available in your community where teenagers can obtain information and counseling. Share your list with your classmates and your friends. The more informed you are about a problem, the greater your chances are of avoiding that problem. Some community resources available to teenagers include their doctors, local health clinics, and community health departments.

Contaceptives One way to reduce the risk of pregnancy is to use condoms and other contraceptives during sexual intercourse. **Contraceptives** are chemicals or devices that are designed to prevent pregnancy. Contraceptives work by stopping a sperm and an egg from joining. The chart below lists contraceptives in order from the most dependable to the least dependable. The use failure rate (UFR) shows how many out of 100 couples would become pregnant in a year using a particular method of contraception. Using a condom in addition to another method of contraception further reduces the risk of pregnancy while it helps prevent AIDS and STD.

contraceptive
(kon′trə sep′tiv), a chemical or device designed to prevent pregnancy.

Methods of Contraception

Method	UFR	How It Works	Special Notes
implant injection	1/300	Hormone prevents ovaries from releasing an egg.	Implant lasts 5 years; 1 injection lasts 3 months.
birth control pill	2/100	Swallowed; prevents ovaries from releasing an egg	Not for smokers; 6 times safer than pregnancy
condom	2-12/100	Worn on penis; keeps sperm from entering the vagina	When used *every* time, UFR is 0-2%; must be held in place at withdrawal
sponge diaphragm	10/100	Inserted in vagina; keeps sperm from entering uterus	Can be hard to remove; slight risk of infections
foam, film, creams, and suppositories	18/100	Released into vagina; immobilizes and kills sperm	All but film are somewhat messy.
withdrawal	20/100	Male removes penis from vaginia before ejaculation.	Risky; sperm often are in pre-ejaculatory fluid; male may not be able to control ejaculation.
no method	85/100	Couple thinks pregnancy will not happen to them.	Every year, one million teenagers become pregnant.

natural family planning, (NFP), a method of contraception in which a couple tries to predict the day of ovulation and abstains from sex a certain number of days before, during, and after ovulation.

Another method called **natural family planning (NFP)** is used by those who prefer not to use contraceptives. NFP requires knowing in advance when ovulation takes place. Then the couple must abstain from sex for a certain number of days before, during, and after ovulation. Teenagers are not good candidates for NFP. It takes 6 months to learn when ovulation takes place before using this method. Also, the woman must have a regular ovulation-menstruation (O-M) cycle. Most teenage girls do not have regular O-M cycles. Therefore, the risk of pregnancy is high for teenagers.

Several other methods of contraception prevent pregnancy permanently. Because they are permanent, most married couples wait until they have their families well established before considering any of these options. These are not recommended for teenagers because of their permanence.

Information about contraceptives and their safe use is easily available to teenagers. Finding out about contraceptives is much less difficult and costly than dealing with an unwanted pregnancy. You can get information about contraceptives from your parents, your doctor, the school nurse or counselor, a health clinic, or your local health department. Some clinics have special hours or special classes for teenagers. The person in the picture is talking to a counselor about contraceptives and risks of pregancy.

Anyone who has sexual intercourse risks pregnancy, even with the best types of contraception. The only sure way to avoid a pregnancy and other problems, such as STD, is *abstinence,* saying no to sexual intercourse and other initimate sexual activity.

Abstinence You learned about abstinence in Chapter 1 and earlier in this chapter. Abstinence means not having sexual intercourse or other intimate sexual behaviors with another person. Abstinence means saying no and requires self-discipline. It helps you have satisfying social and emotional relationships with people of the opposite sex without giving in to bodily feelings.

Practicing abstinence during the teen years will help you avoid pregnancy and other problems, such as sexually transmitted diseases. It will help you become a faithful marriage partner. Even married people practice abstinence at times during their lives together, such as during illnesses or separation.

How can a teenager stay abstinent in a world that seems to encourage early sexual behavior? There are lots of ways. First, you can choose friends of both sexes who share your sexual lifestyle. Friends who have chosen to be abstinent can give each other support when they say no. They will not put pressure on others to behave in ways they do not want to. People who push others to do things they do not want to do are not really caring friends.

Secondly, you can learn to judge situations. You can avoid situations that discourage abstinence. Instead, you can do things that encourage abstinence, like being with people your own age, group dating, participating in activities, avoiding drugs, and not spending long times alone with your boyfriend or girlfriend. Planning ahead helps you avoid pressure for intimate sexual behavior before you are ready. The teenagers in the pictures are happy. They spend time together but in ways that promote abstinence.

Chapter 3 Review

Part I. Write the numbers 1–10 on your paper. Match each definition in Column A with a term from Column B.

Column A

1. development of a baby inside a woman's uterus
2. surest way to prevent pregnancy and STDs
3. source of information about pregnancy
4. problem for many teenage parents
5. source of health problems for pregnant mother
6. expects the father to support his child financially
7. ending of a pregnancy before the developing baby can survive
8. people who support each other in abstinence
9. situation that encourages abstinence
10. methods for preventing pregnancy

Column B

a. abstinence
b. poor nutrition
c. court
d. counselor
e. friends
f. group dating
g. miscarriage
h. poverty
i. pregnancy
j. contraception

Part II. Write the numbers 11–20 on your paper. Answer the following in complete sentences.

11. What are three social problems teenage parents face?
12. Why is good nutrition important for teenage mothers?
13. Name two health risks that teenage mothers face.
14. What are the healthiest ages to have a baby?
15. What are two ways a teenager can promote abstinence?
16. What often happens when a teenage mother lives with her family?
17. How can a person prevent a teenage pregnancy?
18. Give two situations that encourage abstinence.
19. What do many family courts expect of a father?
20. What are two sources of information about preventing pregnancy?

Chapter

4

AIDS and Other Sexually Transmitted Diseases

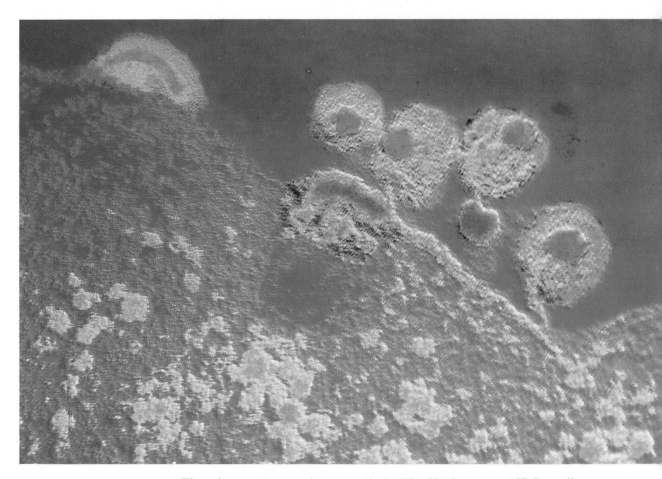

The picture shows viruses called HIV. HIV causes AIDS, a disease in which HIV destroys the body's ability to fight off diseases. AIDS is a world-wide epidemic. Every fifteen seconds, someone is infected with HIV. Scientists are working to develop a vaccine or find a cure for AIDS. In this chapter, you will learn how to avoid getting AIDS and other sexually transmitted diseases.

Pathogens

- in air
- on hands
- on drinking glasses and
  eating utensils
- on objects like pencils
  and phones

New Host

**The Spread of Sexually
Transmitted Diseases**

Host

Pathogens in certain body
fluids passed through
intimate sexual contact

New Host

pathogens (path′ə jəns).
germs that cause a disease.

**sexually transmitted dis-
ease(s), or STD,** a disease
or diseases passed from person to person through sexual
contact.

The Spread of Sexually
Transmitted Diseases

You have probably had a cold or the flu at least once in your life.
The germs that cause these diseases live for a long time in the air,
or on drinking glasses, or unwashed hands. Disease-causing germs
are called **pathogens.**

Pathogens such as cold and flu viruses cause communicable
diseases, which spread from one person to another. The person infected with the pathogen is called a host, or carrier. The first flow
chart shows the different ways that pathogens for typical communicable diseases can leave the host's body. When other persons receive the pathogens from a host, they become new carriers, and the
disease is passed on.

Diseases caused by pathogens that live in the air are easily
spread from one person to another. Other diseases are much harder
to catch. They are caused by pathogens that die quickly when exposed to heat, light, and air. People pass these pathogens to each
other through the direct contact or exchange of blood or certain
other body fluids. This can occur during sexual intercourse or other
sexual contact. Diseases of this type are called **sexually transmitted diseases.** You may have heard them called by an old name—
venereal diseases, or VD. Look at the flow chart for sexually transmitted diseases to see how these different types of pathogens are
spread.

Sexually transmitted diseases, or STD, are passed from an infected person to another person when moist membranes touch other
moist membranes. STD are not transferred by casual contact, like
shaking hands. You cannot catch STD from door knobs, towels,
toilet seats, or swimming pools. However, you could get a disease
like AIDS or hepatitis B by receiving blood from an infected person without any sexual contact.

Because of the way that STD spread, people have a greater
chance of getting a disease if they have sexual contact with more
than one person. People who have many sexual contacts are at high
risk of getting an STD. Did you know that most cases of these diseases are found in people between the ages of 15 and 25? However, people of any age can get STD.

AIDS: A New Epidemic

The first cases of AIDS in the United States were reported in 1981. The chart shows that the number of AIDS cases has grown each year. New infection rates are growing especially fast in young heterosexual females and males. In 1993, AIDS was the sixth leading cause of death to people between the ages of 15 and 24 in the United States.

AIDS is a world health concern because it is a leading cause of death. Scientists hope to develop a vaccine to prevent AIDS by the year 2000. Finding a cure for AIDS may take longer. The best prevention is learning how to avoid getting HIV infection and AIDS.

AIDS means **acquired immune deficiency syndrome.** AIDS is caused by an unusual virus called HIV. HIV weakens the body's natural system of defense against pathogens, called the **immune system.** Normally, your body has plenty of white blood cells called **T-helper cells,** now usually called **CD4 + cells.** These cells help other white blood cells fight pathogens that enter the body. They control the release of special proteins called **antibodies** into the bloodstream.

acquired immune deficiency syndrome, or AIDS, STD caused by the a virus, HIV, that attacks certain white blood cells and destroys the body's defense system.

immune system, the body's natural defense system that fights off pathogens

T-helper cell (CD4 + cell), white blood cell that helps other white blood cells fight pathogens by signaling for them to release antibodies into the bloodstream.

antibody (an′ti bod′ē), protein produced by the immune system that attaches to and disarms a pathogen.

The Growth of AIDS Cases in the United States

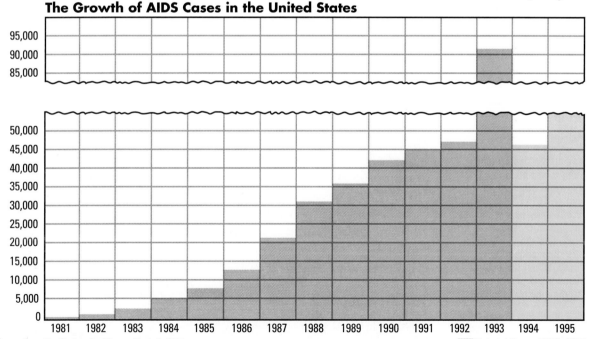

Figures from the Centers for Disease Control, 1994
New CDC case definition guidelines implemented in 1993 dramatically affected the number of cases for that year.

Projected figures (CDC, 1994)

phagocytes (fag′ə sīts), special white blood cells that destroy pathogens.

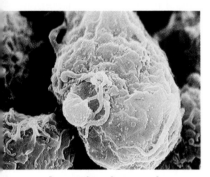

A scanning electron micrograph of an AIDS virus breaking out of a T-helper cell

How HIV Weakens the Immune System

1. HIV enters the body.
2. HIV enters the bloodstream and attaches to and then enters the T-helper and other white blood cells.
3. HIV becomes part of the cell's genetic code.
4. HIV directs the cell to make thousands of new viruses. When the new viruses break out of the cell, they destroy the cell.

Each kind of antibody is made to fight only one specific pathogen. The antibody attaches to a particular pathogen and disarms it. Other white blood cells known as **phagocytes** destroy it. Doctors are able to test a person's blood for the type of antibody that is fighting a disease to find out if that pathogen is in the body.

How does HIV weaken the immune system? Look at the diagram below. When HIV gets into human blood, it invades the T-helper cells and other white blood cells. Once inside, the HIV directs the cell to make thousands of new viruses. As the new viruses break out of the T-helper cell, as shown in the picture, the cell is destroyed. The new viruses go on to attack other T-helper cells.

As the T-helper cells are destroyed, they cannot signal for the release of antibodies to help fight pathogens invading the body. When too many T-helper cells are destroyed, the immune system breaks down. The body cannot fight off diseases.

The good news is that HIV is not very tough. It does not survive in the environment—in the air, on skin, or on surfaces. It is not spread by touching, hugging, or even by normal, closed-mouth kissing. No one who simply lives with a person with AIDS has gotten the disease. The only way to become infected with HIV is to receive into the body certain body fluids, such as blood, from an infected person. Later in this chapter you will learn which behaviors or situations put a person at high risk for becoming infected with HIV.

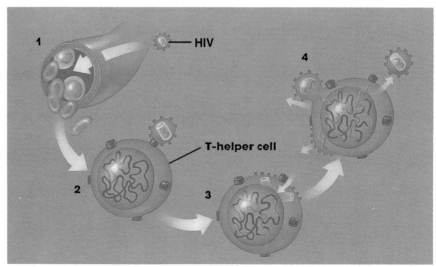

After Lewis E. Calver

The Effects of HIV

When a person receives certain infected body fluids from a person with HIV, the virus enters the body and attacks the T-helper cells in the blood. The remaining healthy T-helper cells signal other cells to produce antibodies to fight the virus. Doctors can test blood to see if it contains antibodies against HIV. If the antibodies are present, the person is infected with HIV. People with HIV are infected for the rest of their lives. This means that, even if they do not yet have the AIDS disease, they can give the virus to others. Scientists estimate that in the mid 1990s, nearly one million Americans are infected with HIV.

Infection Without Symptoms Most people infected with HIV have no visible health problems. Often they do not even know they have the virus. Since it can take 3 to 6 months, or in rare cases longer, for antibodies to appear in the blood after infection, some infected people might not even test positive. Although these people look and feel healthy, they can infect other people with HIV.

The time line shown below can help you understand the effects of HIV and AIDS. After becoming infected with HIV, a person may show no signs or symptoms of illness for a period of 6 months to 10 years or more. As HIV destroys more and more disease-fighting T-helper cells, the immune system continues to be weakened. This weakened immunity may result in some symptoms of illness that do not yet indicate the presence of AIDS. A person is diagnosed with AIDS only when certain conditions called **opportunistic diseases,** appear. These are rare diseases that a normal immune system is able to resist. Within five years after developing AIDS, most patients have died.

opportunistic diseases, certain rare diseases that could normally be resisted by a healthy immune system but cannot be resisted by a weakened immune system.

The Effects of HIV Infection and AIDS

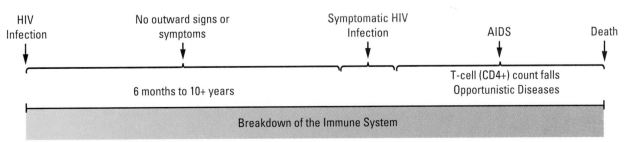

HIV Infection — No outward signs or symptoms — Symptomatic HIV Infection — AIDS — Death

6 months to 10+ years

T-cell (CD4+) count falls
Opportunistic Diseases

Breakdown of the Immune System

symptomatic HIV infection, the period in which an HIV-infected person has symptoms associated with AIDS but before opportunistic diseases or deficient T-cell count occur.

Kaposi's sarcoma (ka po'sez sär kō'mə), a rare skin cancer that is an opportunistic disease affecting persons with AIDS.

PCP, *Pneumocystis carinii* pneumonia, a rare form of pneumonia that is an opportunistic disease affecting persons with AIDS.

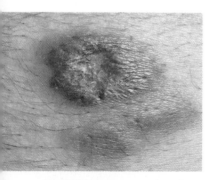

Purple blotches are a sign of Kaposi's sarcoma, an opportunistic disease.

Symptomatic HIV Infection When an HIV-infected person first has symptoms of illness, he or she has **symptomatic HIV infection.** The person loses weight, feels tired, and has swollen glands, night sweats, fever, and diarrhea. The symptoms might last three weeks or longer and then go away and reappear later. Doctors carefully watch patients with symptomatic HIV infection, and often start treatments to delay the onset of AIDS.

AIDS A person is considered to have AIDS when his or her T-helper (CD4+) cell count falls below 200. A healthy person typically has a T-helper cell count of 1,000 or more. Another marker of AIDS is the development of one or more opportunistic diseases. There are now 26 such diseases that are considered markers for AIDS.

Two common opportunistic diseases that affect persons with AIDS are **Kaposi's sarcoma,** a rare skin cancer, and **PCP,** a rare form of pneumonia. Kaposi's sarcoma appears on or under the skin as purple blotches, as shown in the picture. They often appear on the lower legs and feet or around the neck. This fatal cancer also attacks internal organs such as the lining of the mouth, liver, and lungs. The disease PCP infects the lung tissue, causing shortness of breath, weight loss, fever, and weakness. PCP is the most common infection among persons with AIDS, and a leading cause of death.

Other opportunistic diseases include repeat episodes of a certain type of pneumonia, tuberculosis, thrush in the mouth and throat, and cervical cancer in females. HIV might directly attack the cells of the brain, causing difficulty with thinking and remembering. The spinal cord may also be infected. HIV might directly cause cancers. With the assault of diseases and the inability to fight them, the person with AIDS eventually dies.

Risk Behaviors for Getting AIDS

You must receive certain body fluids from an HIV-infected person in order to get the virus. The only body fluids that can spread HIV are blood, blood products, semen, fluids from the vagina, and, in rare cases, breast milk.

Although AIDS was first found in homosexual or bisexual men and in injecting drug users, it can spread to anyone exposed to HIV. AIDS is a top ten killer of 15- to 24-year-olds today. You can protect yourself from HIV infection and AIDS by avoiding these risk behaviors.

Risk Behavior 1: Intimate Sexual Contact You can become infected with HIV through intimate sexual contact. This includes sexual intercourse and other behaviors in which a person's sex organs touch or enter the openings of another person's body. During such contact, fluids containing HIV can be transmitted from the infected person's body to a new host. HIV can enter the uninfected person's body and begin a new infection. The more people with whom someone has sexual contact, the greater the risk for becoming infected with HIV and developing AIDS.

Risk Behavior 2: Injecting Drugs. You can become infected with HIV by using needles or syringes that contain blood from an infected person. When a person uses a dirty needle or syringe, infected blood enters the body of the new host. Drug users, including steroid users, who share drug-use equipment are at great risk. Even sharing needles for piercing ears is dangerous.

Risk Behavior 3: Mother to Baby Pregnant women infected with HIV can transmit the virus to their unborn babies. The virus can pass through the placenta to the baby or the baby can be infected passing through the vagina during birth. Rarely, HIV can be passed from an infected mother to her baby through breast milk.

It is rare to become infected with HIV through a blood transfusion. In 1985, hospitals and the American Red Cross began testing all blood for HIV antibodies. *You cannot get HIV by giving blood. New, clean needles are always used to draw blood.*

Health-care workers can get infected with HIV if stuck by a contaminated needle or if blood gets into their eyes or open cuts or scratches. This laboratory worker is wearing protective gear while working with blood. Doctors, dentists, and nurses use similar techniques to protect themselves from becoming infected.

Laboratory workers can protect themselves from possible infected blood by wearing gloves and a mask and by working behind a glass shield.

Protecting Yourself from HIV Infection and AIDS

Protecting Yourself from HIV Infection and AIDS

- Abstain from intimate sexual behaviors.
- Avoid injecting drugs.
- Limit sexual contact to one uninfected partner.
- Use latex condoms during *every* sexual contact.

mutual monogamy (myü′chü əl mə nog′ə mē), each person having only one sexual partner during a lifetime.

CDC AIDS Hotlines:
English
1-800-342-AIDS (2437)
Spanish (Español)
1-800-344-7432
Hearing-impaired
1-800-243-7889

Sometimes people become infected with HIV without knowing they are at risk. There are steps you can take to avoid becoming infected. The chart summarizes the steps. *The first and most effective way is to practice abstinence*. Abstinence means avoiding sexual intercourse and other intimate sexual contact with another person.

The second way to avoid becoming infected with HIV is to avoid injecting drugs. You can keep yourself healthy and mentally alert by not using *any* harmful drugs. Drugs such as alcohol, marijuana, and cocaine or crack reduce your ability to think clearly and make wise judgments about your behavior.

You can greatly reduce your chances of getting HIV by being abstinent and drug-free during your school years. If you choose friends who also plan to be abstinent and drug-free, you will feel less pressure about sex and drugs. Many students stay away from activities that might weaken their decision to be abstinent. The longer you wait for an intimate sexual relationship, the more likely you will have only one partner for life, which is called **mutual monogamy.** When each person is not infected and has only one partner, there is no sexual risk of getting HIV infection and AIDS.

Studies show that using a latex condom *every time* during *all* intimate sexual behaviors greatly lowers the risk of getting HIV. HIV does not pass through the latex material of condoms. Information about condoms and the correct way to use them is available through the local health department, a doctor, a clinic, or the CDC National AIDS Hotlines, listed at the left.

Testing and Treatment for HIV Infection and AIDS

People can find out if they are infected with HIV by having their blood tested at the local health department, doctor's office, or special testing clinic. The test used to identify antibodies for HIV in blood is called an ELISA test. If the ELISA test is positive, another test, called the Western blot test, is used to check the results. The combination of these two tests is very accurate.

If a person has been infected with HIV within the past few months, all these tests may be negative because the body has not had enough time to produce antibodies. Researchers are continuing to develop new, more accurate tests for detecting HIV.

Today, people with HIV infection and AIDS are living longer and healthier lives than during the first decade of AIDS. Cases are being detected earlier. Doctors know more about managing HIV infection and controlling opportunistic diseases. Drugs such as ZDV (the new name for AZT), ddl, and ddC can help delay, but not cure, AIDS. They are costly drugs and cause some negative side effects. Other drugs can prevent or reduce the effects of PCP. Chemotherapy has helped treat Kaposi's sarcoma.

People who have AIDS need to take good care of themselves. They need to live in clean surroundings, eat balanced meals, exercise if possible, and keep a positive mental attitude. AIDS patients, like other people with serious diseases, need a lot of care and understanding from family and friends.

In this crystal of ZDV, each color represents a different chemical that forms the drug.

The Impact of AIDS on Society

The World Health Organization estimates that 14 million of the world's people have been infected with HIV thus far. By the year 2000, 40 million people are expected to become infected. Scientists believe that more than 110 million people could die of AIDS before the epidemic declines.

Most of the world's AIDS cases are young and middle-aged heterosexual people. AIDS cases in the United States are growing fastest in women and teenage girls. The growth rate of AIDS cases among heterosexual males is faster now than that of drug users who inject drugs.

AIDS is a costly disease. Caring for one person with AIDS for a year in the United States costs about $40,000. The chart shows the increase in medical costs for AIDS treatment from 1986 to 1994. Research, testing, education, and loss of work result in additional costs. Meanwhile, the only effective way to prevent AIDS is avoiding behaviors that spread HIV.

Estimated Costs in Dollars of Medical Care for AIDS in the United States

Year	Cost
1986	1.1 billion
1991	2.4 billion
1993	5.4 billion
1994	6.1 billion*

*Projected from estimated number of living cases (CDC, 1994).

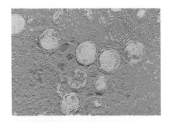

Chlamydia bacteria

chlamydia (klə mid′ē ə), an STD caused by a bacterium that infects the reproductive tracts of both females and males.

sterile, unable to have children.

genital herpes (jen′ə təl hėr′pēz), an STD caused by a virus and producing blisters on the penis, vaginal area, or other areas.

Herpes viruses

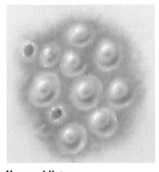

Herpes blisters

Four Common Sexually Transmitted Diseases

Four of the most common sexually transmitted diseases (STD) are chlamydia, herpes, gonorrhea, and syphilis. More than half of all reported cases of STD occur in people under 25 years of age.

Chlamydia The bacteria, shown in the picture, infect the male or female reproductive tract and cause **chlamydia.** Signs of this disease include a pus-like fluid coming out of the penis or vagina and pain or tingling during urination. There may be no symptoms at all, especially in females, making the risk of spread especially high.

If untreated, chlamydia and another STD known as gonorrhea can lead to pelvic inflammatory disease, or PID, which affects a woman's fallopian tubes. PID may leave a person **sterile,** or unable to have children. Without treatment, the urinary organs of males may be badly damaged by chlamydia. People with chlamydia are at increased risk for HIV infection if exposed. This disease can be cured with antibiotics.

Herpes Have you ever had a fever blister on your lips? If so, you have had a mild illness known as herpes. It is caused by a virus. One form of herpes occurs around the genitals and is often called **genital herpes.** A person with genital herpes usually gets blisters on the penis, around the vagina, or in other genital areas. The pictures show the herpes virus and blisters. The blisters appear anywhere from 2 to 20 days after sexual contact. These painful blisters fill with fluid, then burst, form scabs, and finally heal.

Herpes is spread by direct skin-to-skin contact with the infected site, even if there are no noticeable symptoms. Many people with herpes have repeated flare-ups of the symptoms, usually when they are tired or emotionally upset. So far, there is no cure for herpes, but pain can be relieved with a drug.

Genital herpes can cause other serious problems. When sores are present, there is an increased risk that exposure to HIV will lead to infection. Genital herpes can harm an unborn baby as it passes down the mother's birth canal. Almost half of these babies die. Fortunately, most pregnant women with herpes have normal pregnancies. It is important for a pregnant woman with herpes to tell her doctor in order to provide the best medical management for the baby.

Gonorrhea Like chlamydia, **gonorrhea** is an STD caused by bacteria, shown in the upper picture. It infects the urethra and the cervix of women, the urethra of men, and other parts of the body. Its symptoms are similar to chlamydia. Many women and some men have no symptoms. A doctor can test people to find out if they are infected with the bacteria. Gonorrhea, if untreated, causes scar tissue, which may leave both men and women sterile.

If gonorrhea gets into the bloodstream, it can damage the joints, liver, and skin. Gonorrhea can also lead to pelvic inflammatory disease in women. It spreads harmful bacteria in the body, and lack of immediate care may cause death. Antibiotics will cure gonorrhea once it is detected.

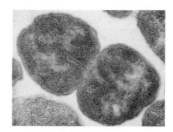

Gonorrhea bacteria

Syphilis Another STD caused by a bacterium is **syphilis**. Syphilis occurs in three stages. During the first stage, a **chancre** appears at the site where the bacteria entered the body. This is usually on the tip of the penis or at the opening of the vagina. The pictures show the syphilis bacteria and chancre. The chancre is about the size of your little fingernail. Surprisingly, the sore usually causes no pain.

The chancre appears about 3 weeks after sexual contact and will go away in about 2 weeks, with or without treatment. However, the disease is still in the body. A visit to a doctor or health department is important if any sore like this appears.

During the second stage of syphilis, a person may feel symptoms of other common illnesses. These symptoms include a mild fever, swollen glands, sore throat, rash, and achy joints. Because of this, syphilis has been called the "great imitator." The second stage usually occurs within 6 to 20 weeks of the first stage.

gonorrhea (gahn′uh rē′uh), an STD caused by a bacteria that enters the body through moist membranes.

syphilis (sif′ə lis), an STD caused by a bacterium that enters the body through injured skin or moist membrane contact; occurs in three stages.

chancre, (shang′kər), a small, round, painless sore that appears as a symptom of syphilis.

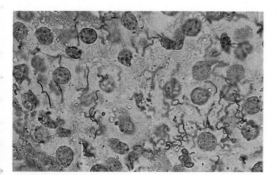

Syphilis bacteria

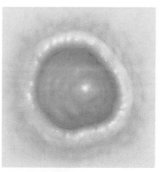

Syphilis chancre

The third stage of syphilis may not appear for 3 to 20 years or more. During the third stage of the disease, tissues and organs are destroyed, causing blindness, mental illness, heart disease, and often death. If treated before the third stage, syphilis can be cured with penicillin or other antibiotics.

Other Sexually Transmitted Diseases

Did you know that a person can have more than one STD at the same time, and can catch the disease again even after being cured? Look at the chart below for facts about other common STD. Notice their causes, symptoms, effects, and treatment. STD are becoming more difficult to treat because they are becoming resistant to the medicines that are used to cure them. Some STD are not yet curable at all.

Disease (Germ)	Symptoms	Long-Term Effects	Treatment
genital warts, or human papilloma virus (HPV) (virus)	Painless, cauliflower-like growths or flat bumps on penis or vagina area.	Five strains are associated with cervical cancer in females.	Growths can be removed. There is no cure; warts can reoccur. Females should have annual PAP test to check for cervical cancer.
vaginitis Candida Monilia (yeasts) trichomoniasis (protozoa)	Burning, itching. Pain with urination. "Cottage cheese" discharge. Foul-smelling, foamy green discharge; redness, burning, itching. Males usually have no signs.	Discomfort	Can be cured with a drug. All partners must be treated at the same time.
NSU or *NGU* (several kinds of bacteria) mycoplasms	Discharge, green or yellowish and thick; inflammation and burning. Frequent urination. Females usually have no signs.	Blocked tubes cause sterility. PID in females. Risk to unborn babies.	Antimicrobial medicine cures NGU or NSU.
hepatitis B (virus)	Skin and whites of eyes turn yellow. Fever, nausea, abdominal pain. Some persons have no symptoms.	Liver damage. Can be fatal.	Usually resolves spontaneously, but damage may remain. Must avoid alcohol.

Prevention of Sexually Transmitted Diseases

The best approach to STD is to prevent them in the first place. Abstinence is the best way to keep from getting AIDS and other sexually transmitted diseases. You always have the right to say no to any risk behavior that might expose you to AIDS or other STD.

More and more teenagers are choosing abstinence because they want to be healthy and have a safe future. If a sexual relationship occurs later in your adult life, mutual monogamy and the use of condoms can reduce the risk of getting AIDS and other STD. As with all diseases, knowing the warning signs and seeking early treatment helps your chances of being cured.

The common signs of STD are listed in the chart. If you notice any of these signs, you should visit your doctor or health department right away for a checkup. If an STD is discovered, your partner should also seek medical treatment. The boy in the picture is talking to a doctor about STD during a checkup. Visits like this are private and kept confidential. If you have questions about STD, you can call the American Social Health Service's National STD Hotline, listed to the right.

Common Warning Signs of STDs

- Pus-like fluid coming from penis or vagina
- Itching, burning, rash or pain around penis or vagina
- Blisters, sores or growths in the gential area
- Need to urinate frequently
- Pain with urination
- Bad smelling odor from genitals
- Swollen glands and fever

National Sexually Transmitted Diseases Hotline: 1–800–227–8922

Your doctor can give you information about preventing STD and can run tests to check for an STD.

Chapter 4 Review

*Part I. Write the numbers 1–10 on your paper. Match each
definition in Column A with a term from Column B.*

Column A

1. a disease caused by HIV
2. abbreviation for a disease spread through sexual contact
3. germs that cause diseases
4. an STD that occurs in three stages
5. a protein released into the blood that fights a certain pathogen
6. an opportunistic disease
7. the period in which an HIV-infected person has symptoms associated with AIDS but before opportunistic diseases or deficient T-cell count occur
8. an STD that may lead to pelvic inflammatory disease, if untreated.
9. a special white blood cell that helps other white blood cells fight pathogens
10. unable to have children

Column B

a. AIDS
b. antibody
c. chlamydia
d. symptomatic HIV infection
e. pathogens
f. PCP
g. STD
h. sterile
i. syphilis
j. T-helper cell

*Part II. Write the numbers 11–20 on your paper. Answer the
following in complete sentences.*

11. How does HIV infection make people ill?
12. What are two ways to avoid getting STD?
13. Name the three risk behaviors for becoming infected with HIV.
14. List four common warning signs of STD.
15. Name two ways to protect yourself from HIV infection.
16. Name four common sexually transmitted diseases.
17. Why is it especially important for females with genital warts to have an annual PAP test?
18. What is symptomatic HIV infection?
19. Describe what opportunistic diseases are and give examples of two such diseases.
20. Why is early medical treatment important for STD?

5

Preventing and Coping with Sexual Abuse

This girl is calling her family for a ride home from the library. She had planned to walk the six blocks home after studying. However, her work took her longer than she expected, and now it is dark outside. She is not taking any chances and knows how to stay safe.

In this chapter, you will learn about staying safe and preventing sexual abuse. You will also learn where to turn for help in coping with sexual abuse.

Types of Sexual Abuse

In this book you have read about the different changes that occur during adolescence as you reach sexual maturity. You learned how to keep yourself free of sexually transmitted diseases and how to avoid teenage pregnancy. You also need to be aware of sexual abuse and how to keep yourself safe.

sexual (sek′ shu el) **abuse**, improper sexual behavior.

Sexual abuse is improper sexual behavior. It occurs when someone takes advantage of another person against his or her will. The victim usually feels powerless to avoid or stop the sexual abuse. Sexual abuse includes incest, sexual assault, sexual harrassment, and pornography.

Preventing Sexual Abuse

incest (in′ sest), sexual activity between family members.

When a family member sexually abuses another family member, it is called **incest**. This includes any form of sexual activity between family members, whether between blood relatives or stepparents or stepchildren. Children and adolescents are often victims of incest. They also can be victims of sexual abuse by other people they know. The abuser might begin with unnecessary fondling, and then take sexual advantage of the youth. Young people are sometimes afraid to say no to sexual abuse because they have been taught to listen to family members and adults. They might feel too afraid or ashamed to tell anyone. However, young people who have been sexually abused should not feel at fault for what has happened.

Say no in a firm voice.

Get away.

Tell an adult you trust.

The pictures show three ways you can stop sexual abuse. First, say no in a firm voice. Second, leave if you possibly can. Third, find an adult you trust and tell him or her what has happened. Teachers, counselors, and youth leaders know ways to help you stop sexual abuse. Keep talking until you get action.

When physical force or violence is used with sexual abuse, it is called sexual assault. One type of sexual assault is **rape,** which is forcing a person into sexual intercourse against his or her will. Most rapes are committed by men against women. Many victims are teenage girls. Boys and men also can be victims of sexual assault. Rape is not for sexual pleasure but is meant to hurt and humiliate the other person.

Sometimes rapists are strangers. However, rapists often know their victims. Rapists try to catch their victims off guard. Rape usually happens in houses or cars, but it can happen at parties, dances, or in dark, deserted places like woods or beaches.

Teenagers can learn to protect themselves from rape. They can avoid going out alone at night by always walking or riding with friends or family. Keeping the car or house locked at all times is also important. People need to stay aware of their surroundings and plan ahead. Stay alert. If someone seems to be acting in a strange way—they block your way, get too close, or stare—quickly move away toward other people and safety. If someone does attack you, yell for help. Some experts recommend yelling, ''Fire!'' This confuses the rapist, and people usually come running.

Teenage girls may be threatened with date rape. **Date rape** occurs when a girl's date forces her to engage in sexual behavior against her will. Her date may use physical force, threats, or pressure. Sometimes, date rape results from unclear communication. Some people send out mixed messages. They might say no with their voice but say yes with their behavior or body. To prevent any problems, people need to clearly communicate their own limits for sexual behavior. If a girl says no and a boy forces her into sexual activity against her will, legally it is rape. Date rape is a serious offense. If you do not feel right about the direction things are heading, stop the behavior and say no.

Most states have laws against **statutory rape,** which involves sexual behavior with a girl under a certain age even if she agrees to the activity. The age varies from state to state.

rape, forcing a person to engage in sexual intercourse against his or her will.

date rape, forcing a person to have sexual intercourse during a date.

statutory (stach′ u̇ tôr′ē) **rape,** unlawful sexual intercourse with a female who is below a legal age, with or without her consent.

Ways to Stay Safe from Sexual Abuse

1. Say no.
2. Avoid going out at night alone.
3. Keep car and house locked.
4. Stay alert to surroundings.
5. Try to get away, or yell for help.
6. Tell someone you trust.

Dealing with Sexual Harassment and Pornography

Sexual abuse is not only a physical form of abuse. People can abuse others with words or actions. When a person uses words to torment or threaten another person about sex, it is called **sexual harassment**. Sexual harassment is illegal. Both men and women have been convicted of this crime. You can stop someone from sexually harassing you by telling them you will report them if they do not leave you alone. Avoid the company of the person who is harassing you. Tell a parent, teacher, counselor, or the police about the problem. You do not have to listen to such abuse.

sexual harassment
(sek′ shü el har′əs ment, hə ras′ment), when a person threatens or torments another person about sex.

Parents can help their son or daughter find ways to stop sexual harassment.

Sexual harassment can harm a person's mental health and lower his or her self-esteem. So can behaving in a way that conflicts with a person's values. You may care for certain people and want to please them. However, if they ask you to do something that you feel is not right, you should refuse. If they really care about you, they will understand. If they still insist, they are sexually exploiting you—using you for their own selfish purposes.

Pornography usually is a form of sexual exploitation. Pornography is pictures or other material used to cause sexual excitement. When children are the subjects of pornography, they are being exploited. Pornography gives false ideas and attitudes about sexual activities. It does not show loving, caring relationships.

pornography
(pôr nog′rə fē), pictures or other material used to cause sexual excitement.

Coping with Sexual Abuse

Although sexual abuse can sometimes be prevented, a person might not be able to escape from the attacker. How can a person cope with the effects of sexual abuse after it happens? Anyone who has been raped or sexually abused needs medical attention and emotional support.

Victims of sexual assault need medical care from a hospital, emergency room, or clinic. Doctors will give the victim medical care and later can testify that sexual abuse has occurred. Victims should not clean up before going for medical care because they might destroy needed evidence.

A person who has been attacked sexually should contact the police. Most experts believe that victims should press charges against the person who abused them. Otherwise, the abuser might repeat the crime again and again. Also, some local police departments have an assistance program for rape victims.

Getting emotional support is important to help victims cope with the trauma of sexual abuse. Most cities and towns have rape crisis centers. Counselors, teachers, or parents can help victims get the services they need. Counselors also can help sexual abuse victims and their families cope. The picture shows a **support group** of people who have been abused. A support group gives individuals the encouragement and friendship they need to help them recover emotionally.

support group, people with similar experiences who share their feelings to help them cope with problems.

A support group can help a victim recover from the emotional effects of sexual abuse.

Chapter 5 Review

Part I. Write the numbers 1–10 on your paper. Match each definition in Column A with a term from Column B.

Column A

1. a general term for all types of improper sexual behavior
2. sexual intercourse with a girl under a certain age
3. using words to threaten or torment about sexual behavior
4. pictures or other material used to cause sexual excitement
5. one way to prevent date rape
6. sexual activity between family members
7. abuse victims who talk together about their feelings
8. people who can help victims of abuse
9. type of immediate help needed by someone who has been sexually assaulted
10. forcing a person into sexual intercourse against his or her will

Column B

a. clear communication
b. counselors
c. incest
d. medical care
e. pornography
f. rape
g. sexual abuse
h. sexual harassment
i. statutory rape
j. support group

Part II. Write the numbers 11–20 on your paper. Answer the following in complete sentences.

11. What three steps should a person take to stop sexual abuse?
12. Explain why the victim of sexual abuse should not feel at fault.
13. Who is most often the victim of a rape?
14. What are four types of sexual abuse?
15. List three people who can help you stop sexual abuse.
16. What are four ways teenagers can protect themselves from rape?
17. How do support groups help people cope with sexual abuse?
18. Why is clear communication important between people who are dating?
19. List two forms of sexual exploitation.
20. Explain what statutory rape means.

6

Developing Life Management Skills

These friends share many different kinds of experiences as they go through the changes of adolescence. Like other teenagers, these adolescents are learning more about themselves and how to cope with peer pressure. They are also developing other important life management skills, such as how to make wise decisions and how to communicate their thoughts and feelings to others. These skills will help them lead responsible, happy lives as adults.

Coping with Media and Peer Pressure

In this booklet, you have read about many of the changes that occur during adolescence. As you experience these changes, you develop into the person you will be as an adult. You learn about your likes, dislikes, talents, and dreams. You begin to form ideas about who you are. These ideas make up your **self-concept**.

Part of your self-concept involves how you judge yourself—whether you feel good or bad about who you are. People who like themselves have good **self-esteem**. Most people feel better about themselves some days than others. Doing things that go along with their values makes them feel good about themselves and can improve their self-esteem. Such activities might include practicing a sport, studying and doing well on exams, or helping a friend.

self-concept, the ideas a person has about himself or herself.

self-esteem, the positive feelings a person has about himself or herself.

media (mē′dē ə), television, radio, newspapers, magazines, books, and other means of communication.

Media Your family, friends, and the **media** influence your self-concept and self-esteem. Examples of media include television, radio, newspapers, magazines, books, and billboards. Media inform us about the world around us and also provide entertainment. However, media can take up much of our time, leaving little time for real life experiences and relationships.

Media can affect the way you feel about yourself by showing you a glamorous fantasy that looks very real. If you compare yourself to these fantasies, you might feel incomplete. You might feel you should have few problems or solve problems easily like some people on TV or in the movies. However, many of these media images are not real. Remember that TV programs and movies are meant to entertain, and movie and TV stars are paid to act. Most people do not live their lives the way you see them in the media.

You might see values represented in the media that are different from your own. Such values could include pleasure-seeking, getting what you want now rather than waiting, thinking only about the present, or trying to be like others in a group. However, your values or those of your family might involve working to become successful, putting off certain things until the time is right, or being a strong individual. You have learned that behaving according to your values raises your self-esteem. Learning to evaluate realistically what you see and hear in the media can help build your self-esteem.

Peer Pressure Besides the media, your friends play an important role in how you see yourself as a person. Friends and other people in your age group are called **peers**. You have learned how adolescents seek friendships with their peers. These friendships provide support and security during times of change. Peers can have a strong influence on your self-esteem by making you feel good or bad about yourself. The influence of peers is called **peer pressure**. Learning to deal with peer pressure is a big step in growing up.

Peer pressure can be positive. For example, a boy is injured while playing basketball with his friends. He wants to stay in the game to help his teammates. His friend convinces him to stop and go see a doctor because his nose might be broken.

Friends can also put negative pressure on you to do something that goes against your better judgment or your values. You might not always want to do what your peers are doing, but you might be afraid they will not like you unless you go along with them. The boy in the picture is feeling this kind of pressure. How is he handling the situation? What could he do if they keep trying to pressure him? He could say no again and walk away. He knows that true friends respect each other's opinions and feelings. They will accept him even if he does not do everything they do.

If you feel pressure to do something you do not want to do, remember that you, and not your friends, must live with the results of your behavior. Doing things that go against your values, even with friends, might lower your self-esteem.

peers, people of the same age group.

peer pressure, the strong influence people of the same age group sometimes have on one another.

"No thanks! I'd rather not."

Developing Refusal Skills

refusal skills, ways to say no to negative peer pressure.

Practicing Refusal Skills

Line: "Come on, everybody else is doing it."
Response: "I'm not everybody. I'm somebody."

Line: "If you really love me, you'll do this for me."
Response: "If you really love me, you'll stop pressuring me."

Action: Your date tries to hold you or touch you in a way you do not like.
Response: Move the person's hands away and say, "Please stop. I'm not comfortable with this."

One way to handle peer pressure is to learn **refusal skills**—ways to say no. Sometimes you just have to say no directly. You can do it in a serious way or use humor. Let your friends know that you care about them, even though you will not do what they want.

Sometimes peer pressure involves sexual activity. A person might use a line to try to persuade a girlfriend or boyfriend to be sexually intimate. Throughout this booklet you have learned that the practice of abstinence—saying no to intimate sexual activity—is the surest way to avoid certain risks, including STDs, AIDS, and pregnancy. Those who practice abstinence can reduce sexual pressure from peers by responding negatively to any line someone might use. Study the lines and responses to the left. They give examples of refusal skills using either words or actions.

If the person keeps pressuring you, you can always change the subject, turn away from the person, or suggest that you go do something with friends or go get something to eat. Learning refusal skills like these can help you resist sexual or negative peer pressure. True friends respect your feelings when you let them know the limits of your behavior. These good friendships will give you a sense of belonging, and friends can be good company as you share the ups and downs of adolescence.

Learning to Communicate with Others

Good communication is an important life management skill for getting along with others. Good communication can help you deal with peer pressure. How well do you communicate? People who communicate effectively share feelings, ideas, and viewpoints and understand one another.

Speaking and listening are two parts of communication. Do you talk more than you listen? Do you listen more than you talk? Effective communication involves both good listening and clear speaking. When you talk, try to express yourself clearly. Look at the other person's eyes and face when you talk. If someone does not seem to understand you, say your thought in another way. Be tactful and try to take the other person's feelings into consideration.

Your **body language** may speak as loudly as your words. If you are yawning while someone is talking to you, he or she might think you are not interested in what is being said. People are not always aware of their body language. What messages might the people in the picture be sending to each other? Think about the messages you may be sending someone with your facial expressions or body movements while you communicate.

One part of refusal skills is saying no with body language as well as with words. You might confuse someone if you say you do not want to do something but are smiling and looking happy. The way you dress and behave can also give false messages.

Good listening is just as important to good communication as clear speaking. Active listeners concentrate on what the other person is saying. They try not to interrupt someone or tune them out. They do not think about what they are going to say while the other person is still speaking. Put downs, sarcastic comments, and strong opinions tend to cut off communication. If you are unsure of what someone is saying, try asking questions. Listen for the feelings as well as the words.

Good communicators value the other person's opinion. They get along with people who might not have the same opinions they do because they listen well and explain their own ideas clearly. Good communication does not mean always agreeing with someone. Practicing good communication skills will help you get along with people as an adolescent and later as an adult.

body language, communicating with facial expressions, body movements, and posture.

Learning to Set Goals and Make Decisions

Two of the most important life management skills you will learn during adolescence are how to set goals and how to make wise decisions. These skills will help you deal with the changes of adolescence as well as help you throughout your life.

A **goal** is something that you want to achieve and you work toward. Working toward goals helps build self-esteem. One of the best things about goals is that you choose them for yourself. You can choose long-term goals like becoming an airplane mechanic. You can also choose short-term goals like learning to take apart a small appliance motor and put it together again. Choosing goals and working toward them helps you take control of your life.

Whatever goals you choose, they should be within reach. For example, becoming a rock star might or might not be a reachable goal, but working in the recording industry is achievable. The interests, values, and strengths you have been developing during adolescence help you determine the right goals for you. Goals that are right for you should be your own choice. They should be stated clearly and positively, and they should be reachable within a reasonable amount of time. To achieve a goal, first outline the steps you need to take to get to that goal. Sometimes a series of short-term goals will help you reach a long-term goal.

By setting goals for yourself now and reaching some of those goals, you will gain the confidence and skills you will use as an adult to manage your own life. You will also have a clearer idea of what you want to achieve in the future. This can help you resist pressure to do something that might prevent you from reaching your long-term goals.

Another important life managment skill involves making wise decisions. You can use decision-making skills to solve problems or cope with peer pressure. Study the six steps in the decision-making chart at the left. You can see how the decision-making model works by reading through the example on the next page. First, state the problem and the decision that needs to be made. Then, list all the possible choices. Now look more closely at each choice and consider the consequences. Can you think of any that are not listed on the next page? Remember to think about the long-range outcomes as well as those that affect you now.

goal, something a person wants to do or achieve.

Decision-Making Steps

1. State the decision that needs to be made.
2. List the possible choices.
3. List the possible consequences for each choice.
4. Check each choice with the guidelines for responsible decisions:
   - Is it safe?
   - Is it legal?
   - Is it healthful?
   - Would it be acceptable to my parents and other family members?
   - Is it respectful of myself and others?
5. Select the best choice.
6. Evaluate the decision.

As you list the positive and negative consequences for each choice, check to see if the choice meets the guidelines for responsible decisions listed in step 4. Then select the choice that seems best for you. Finally, evaluate your choice. Do you feel good about it? Will it make you feel good about yourself? If not, start over and see if you left out any possible solutions. This could be a good time to get help from another person, such as as a parent, counselor, or another adult you trust. This person may be able to suggest additional options. When you are happy with the decision, act upon it.

Following the decision-making steps can help you deal with problems you encounter during adolescence. The more you develop goal-setting and decision-making skills now, the better able you will be to set goals and make decisions throughout your life.

Decision-Making Model

The situation: Your boyfriend or girlfriend wants to come over to your house while your parents are away. This is against your parents' rules.

Choice #1: You could let your friend come over and hope your parents will not find out.
Positive Consequences: You would not have to say no to your friend.
Negative Consequences: Your parents could find out, and you would be grounded for a month. Your parents would not trust you anymore. If you break your parents' rules, you will feel guilty. If you and your friend are alone all evening, things could get out of hand.

Choice #2: You could tell your friend it is against your parents' rules.
Positive Consequences: You would not be breaking the rules. Your parents would trust you in the future.
Negative Consequences: You would have to say no to your friend. Your friend might get mad at you or try to pressure you.

Choice #3: You could invite your friend to come over later when your parents are home.
Positive Consequences: You would not be breaking the rules. You would still get to spend time with your friend at home.
Negative Consequences: You would not get to be with your friend right away.

Choice #4: You could go to a ball game or other event instead.
Positive Consequences: You could spend time together doing something you both like. You would not be breaking the rules.
Negative Consequences: Your friend might not want to go.

Chapter 6 Review

Part I. Write the numbers 1–10 on your paper. Match each definition in Column A with a term from Column B.

Column A

1. television, radio, magazines
2. positive feelings you have about yourself
3. something you work toward
4. your ideas about yourself
5. friends and people in your own age group
6. sharing of feelings and opinions with others
7. strong influence of friends on each other
8. communicating with facial expressions
9. a life management skill
10. statement used to persuade a person to be sexually active

Column B

a. body language
b. communication
c. decision making
d. goal
e. line
f. media
g. peer pressure
h. peers
i. self-concept
j. self-esteem

Part II. Write the numbers 11–20 on your paper. Answer the following in complete sentences.

11. Name two uses of media.
12. What is the difference between self-concept and self-esteem?
13. Give an example of positive peer pressure.
14. What are the six steps in decision making?
15. List two elements of good communication.
16. Define what goals are, and give an example of a long-term goal.
17. What can you do if someone uses a line with you?
18. What are the five guidelines for responsible decisions?
19. How does the media influence self-esteem?
20. Give an example of negative peer pressure.

Index

ejaculation, 22
    nocturnal emission, 15
ELISA test, for HIV, 41
emotional changes during adolescence, 9
epididymis, 16
erection, 15
    during sexual intercourse, 22
estrogen, 18

F

Fallopian tubes, 18–20, 22
    cilia, 20
    during ovulation, 20
    during sexual intercourse, 22
fathers, teenage, 26–27
    court attitudes toward, 27
    social problems of, 26, 27
female hormones, 18
    estrogen, 18
    progesterone, 18
fertilization, 20, 22, *illus.* 22
follicle, 20
foreskin, 14
    circumcision, 14
friendship
    during adolescence, 11
    and peer pressure, 55

G

genital herpes, 42
genital warts (human papilloma virus), 44
genitals, 14, 18
    female, 18
        clitoris, 18
        labia, 18
    male, 14
        penis, 14. *See also* penis
        scrotum, 14
glans, 14
goal setting, 58
gonorrhea, 42, 43, *illus.* 43
growth spurt, 7–8
growth stages, of females and males, 7–8

H

health care workers, and risk of AIDS, 39
herpes, 42, *illus.* 42
HIV infection, 37
HIV virus, 35
hormones, 18, 20, 21
    and emotional changes, 9
    female, 18
    and puberty, 7
human papilloma virus (genital warts), 44
hymen, 18

I

immune system, 35–36
    antibodies, 35–36, 37
    opportunitistic diseases, 37–38
    phagocytes, 36
    T-helper cells, 35–36, 37
incest, 48
intimate sexual contact, and risk of HIV, 39
intravenous drug use, and risk of HIV, 39

K–L

Kaposi's sarcoma, 38, *illus.* 38

labia, 18
life management skills, 10–11, 54–59
    decision-making steps, 58–59
    good communication, 56
    media and peer pressure, 54–55
        coping with, 54–55
        on self-esteem, 54–55
    refusal skills, 56

M

marriages, teenage, 26
maturity
    emotional, 6, 8–9, 11, 28
    physical, 6, 7–8, 11, 28
    sexual, 6, 7–8
    social, 6, 9–11, 28
media, influence on self-esteem, 54